<u>Dedication</u>

To you with love and thanks.

Andrea Chatten Msc, MBPsS, PGCL&M, Bed(Hons), Dip.CBT, Dip. Hypnotherapy

Andrea has been a specialised teacher for over 25 years, working with children from ages 5-16 with emotional and behavioural difficulties. She is currently working as 'Lead Children's Emotional & Behavioural Psychologist' at Unravel CEBPC primarily with schools and families in and around the Sheffield area.

Developing positive, trusting relationships has always been at the heart of her practice with children and young people to nudge them into improved psychological well-being. Over the years, Andrea has developed and applied many positive developmental psychology approaches.

This insight is incorporated into her stories, in order to help children, young people and their families to gain more understanding and potential strategies to try to deal with a range of behavioural issues which children and young people could experience. Andrea created 'The Blinks' so that parents could also benefit from reading the books with their children, especially if they identify with the children in the stories and their family circumstances. Both parent and child can learn how to manage early forms of psychological distress as a natural part of growing up, rather than it become problematic when not addressed in its early stages.

'The Blinks' is a series of books which discreetly applies lots of psychological theory throughout the stories, including Cognitive Behavioural Therapy, Developmental and Positive Psychology approaches.

This, book 6 in the series, aims to help children understand how to access and feel the love around them to change negative perceptions and improve well-being.

Book 1 in the series tackles the issue of worry and how to prevent this everyday cognition from becoming a more serious anxiety in the future. Book 2 – Anger helps children understand the physiological aspects of anger, what can trigger it and most importantly, how to control it.

Book 3 – Self-esteem subtly educates children and young people on the importance of liking who they are as well as learning to accept their flaws so that have more realistic expectations of themselves and their well-being.

Book 4 - Sadness helps children and young people to recognise how sad thoughts can be captured and lead to a more persistent low mood. It then provides lots of strategies to help create the much-needed emotional freedom from this difficult feeling.

Book 5 – Shy supports children who may be feeling low in self-confidence or, in more severe situations, experiencing elements of social anxiety. It helps children recognise some of the negative thinking patterns that need to be nudged in order to see things more realistically and rationally.

Introduction

The Blinks books have been created to help children, young people and their families understand more about emotions and how these deep feelings, if not intercepted, can negatively impact on well-being. With a better understanding of what we are feeling and active use of the strategies and techniques provided in this book, we can help support and change the complexity and duration of difficult feelings and behaviours of those in our care.

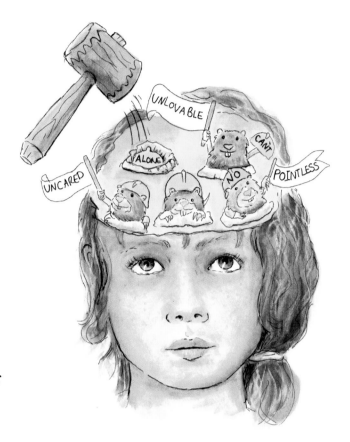

'Love', the sixth Blinks book in this series, follows the story of Morna, a child who doesn't know how to feel love. This affects her in many ways. It impacts on her relationships as she rarely feels close to people. It also affects other emotions as she often feels angry, anxious and sad. More significantly, it reduces her ability to like who she is which makes it even harder for her to feel the love that is around her.

Many children and adults can struggle with feeling loved and it is all intertwined with the strength of relationships with our early caregivers. Love is based on many external factors, including quality of attachment and commitment to care which you will learn more about throughout this manual. Love is also affected by the love we have for ourselves (internal factor), as it is very difficult to feel love if we don't like who we are or feel that we are not loveable.

Life events can impact on the quality of these things very easily. Interestingly, it is suggested that even in the best possible attachment between a caregiver and child, we are only roughly 30% accurate, which means we can get it wrong 70% of the time and our children still have the best secure attachment possible.

Children and parents who struggle to understand and communicate the language of love can develop more complex emotional and behavioural difficulties, underpinned with a low value in who they think they are. The development of self-esteem begins very early and this book will hopefully help to strengthen parental sensitivity to children and young people's needs which has been proven to foster stronger attachment, commitment, positive physical interaction and fundamentally, feelings of love.

Throughout The Blinks' 'Love' novel, help becomes available from Lucy Love-Unlocker who supports Morna on her journey of self-discovery to find out how to feel loved. It incorporates seeking out and learning to lock-in the love that is readily available around us and also helps with the importance of self-love. If we don't love who we are and feel loveable, it is difficult to feel love from others.

As Morna and Lucy Love-Unlocker work together, we get a deeper understanding of what Morna is feeling, and learn effective strategies to help move things forward more effectively. This crucial formula (as shown below) underpins all the information that The Blinks books provide, as it is at the heart of driving positive change and improved well-being:

Understanding/ Insight	**+**	**Strategies/effort/ action**	**=**	**Success/ Positive change/ Happier children & young people**

This book aims to help you, the active and caring adult in a child or young person's life, to understand the psychological theory behind The Blinks' help, which supports Morna and her family to become more emotionally sensitive towards each other and develop stronger feelings of love. The greater our understanding about difficult feelings and how they present, the more confidently we can guide the children and young people in our care in the right direction, which means improved well-being for all.

Section 1 - The Psychology of Love

Love is...

For those of you who remember the two sweet cartoon characters created by Kim Casali in the 1960's (search the web if you haven't, they will bring a smile to your face), love is something that can be quite difficult to define. Fundamentally, love is a core emotion. We could say it is the most important emotion as it can be the catalyst to our sense of self, our well-being, how we manage other emotions and our resilience to cope with life's ups and downs. However, it can be argued that love is a combination of factors, which dictate its strength and intensity and not just one thing.

As emotions are individual and abstract, so defining them is complex. Explaining the core of love has always proved difficult, even going as far back as ancient civilizations. Here are some of the theories of love:

Triangular theory of love (Robert Steinberg 1986)

This model proposes that love is created from three crucial components:

  ✓ Intimacy – emotional closeness, support and care
  ✓ Passion – emotional and psychological encouragement
  ✓ Commitment – the actions required to sustain love over time

Depending on the strength of each of these factors and how they are blended, it is thought that there are eight possible varieties of love:

  1. Non-love – low in all three factors

2. Liking – high in intimacy only

3. Infatuation – high in passion only

4. Empty love – commitment only

5. Romantic love – intimacy and passion

6. Companionate love – intimacy and commitment

7. Fatuous love – passion and commitment

8. Consummate love – intimacy, passion and commitment

The Colour Wheel of Love (John Lee 1973)

This model compares love to the three primary colours and the large variety of colours that can be made from them. He suggests that there are three principal styles of love:

- Eros – meaning passion for physical and emotional connection
- Ludos – the need for play and fun
- Storge – natural affection, peaceful and uncomplicated.

From these key types, some secondary types of love can evolve including:

- Mania – this is what we call obsessive love and is a combination of eros and ludos and is often erratic with extreme highs and lows. Jealousy is often proof of manic love, as it is the constant need for acceptance and reassurance
- Pragma – this is a more practical approach to love and combines ludos and storge. It tends to have more rules, demands and expectations
- Agape – this love is based on eros and storge and is the closest to what we would call unconditional love. It is based on putting another person first and is thought to be love in its purest form.

Compassionate v's Passionate (Elaine Hatfield 1993)

This model suggests two basic kinds of love:

1. Compassionate Love – this is love based on positive attachment, mutual respect, trust and affection and is most likely to last in duration.

2. Passionate Love – this love is grounded in attraction, intense emotions, affection

and elements of anxiety. This kind of love is thought to be short term and will hopefully move towards compassionate love.

What we can see from all of the above models is that the desire for emotional closeness activates the positive attachment we all need and is at the core of all feelings of love. It is also clear that love is a combination of feelings, states of mind, attitudes and behaviours that all contribute to how love is expressed. This lies at the heart of attachment theory, which begins at birth between the child and the major caregiver. Attachment is:

✓ essential to ensure the survival of the child

✓ is a bond of affection that affirms feelings of love and care through contact and attunement. It joins two people emotionally across time and distance

✓ at the heart of physical, social, emotional and cognitive development

✓ positive early attachments that promote resilience to difficult situations later in life

This table below explains the four different attachment styles:

Attachment styles	% of sample (also general-ized to represent U.S. popu-lation)	The child's general state of being	Mother's responsive-ness to her child's sig-nals and needs	Fulfillment of the child's needs (why the child acts the way it does)
Secure Attachment	65%	Secure, explorative, happy	Quick, sensitive, consistent	Believes and trusts that his/her needs will be met
Avoidant Attachment	20%	Not very explorative, emotionally distant	Distant, disengaged	Subconsciously believes that his/her needs probably won't be met
Ambivalent Attachment	10-15%	Anxious, insecure, angry	Inconsistent; sometimes sensitive, sometimes neglectful	Cannot rely on his/her needs being met
Disorganized Attachment	10-15%	Depressed, angry, completely passive, nonrespon-sive	Extreme, erratic: Frightened or frightening, passive or intrusive	Severely con-fused with no strategy to have his/her needs met

From the above table, we can see that our role in emotionally connecting with our child is fundamental to their development and well-being. Yet personality traits, past experiences, traumatic life events and poor parenting can impact on our ability to be able to develop the strong bonds that our children need from us. Attachment can be weakened by:

- pre-birth difficulties
- separation from primary caregiver
- having a negative self-image or low self-esteem that is projected onto the child
- illnesses such as colic or postnatal depression
- inconsistent or inadequate care
- levels of neglect
- traumatic life events like death, domestic violence. These could be unresolved issues in the parent's life or more recent life events
- levels of abuse – physical, emotional and sexual
- cross-generational issues of parenting approaches

It is important to mention here that not all children who present with attachment issues have experienced poor parenting. In many cases, physical or neurological difficulties or the temperament of the child can have a huge impact on their behavioural responses.

Secure attachment is only ever 30% accurate, yet this is enough to ensure that our children develop with a strong sense of self and resilience. We don't need to be constantly kissing our children, interacting with our children or responding to their every need for them to feel loved. In fact, it is now thought that parenting that is too intense and over-controlling (helicopter parenting), can have a negative impact on development as it doesn't allow children to explore, make mistakes and learn to recognise and manage their own emotions or learn to make appropriate choices.

The key to a positive attachment is thought to be parental sensitivity and the ability to read cues from the child and respond accordingly. In some Scandinavian countries, this is taught to parents where positive attachment may be weaker. Even when the parent does not initially feel a strong bond with the child, learning how to respond in ways which affirm connectivity to the child can foster a stronger connection. More importantly, this makes for a happier parent and child which makes the job of parenting so much more pleasurable, even at difficult times.

Here are some ways to develop stronger parental sensitivity:

- ✓ Check in with your own emotional state. We need to be as emotionally stable as possible if we want to send the right affirmations to our children
- ✓ Make your child or young person your top priority and let them know how important they are to you
- ✓ Make sure that you are available when your child needs you, this includes physically, mentally and emotionally. Confirm you are there as a secure base for whatever they need from you. Be present and in the moment as much as possible
- ✓ Patience communicates love to children. Try not to get cross with every negative thing they do or the demands they have on you
- ✓ Even if your child is proving difficult and you are struggling to feel close to them at that time, act as the parent you would like to be. Be the warm, caring, understanding parent that they need
- ✓ Respond appropriately to their needs
- ✓ Communicate often that your child is loved, valued, understood, safe and able to affect change
- ✓ Playing with children breaks down adult-child barriers. Painting and baking are positive ways to interact and share mutually enjoyable time
- ✓ Tell children you love them, often
- ✓ Invest time, energy and determination. They are worth it and you will reap the rewards with happier children

When we activate a positive attachment with our children it helps the child to thrive.

☺ • Children will reach full cognitive potential as they feel safe to explore, experiment and learn

☺ • Children will develop a strong sense of self-esteem and well-being as they feel loved and valued

☺ • Emotional intelligence begins to develop as they feel safe to express feelings and so begin to understand them, learn to express them appropriately and regulate them at difficult times. They also begin to recognise the feelings of others and so begin to exercise empathy

☺ • Children with positive attachment also develop good interpersonal skills and feel able to communicate their needs, as they know they have a support system available to them

As we can see, the psychology of love is very complex and based on many variables that can impact on the quality that children receive. Nevertheless, as with life, being reflective as a parent is the greatest factor in improving things for the better between you and your child. It will never make us perfect, but it will hopefully prevent us from making the same mistakes which may lead to more problematic outcomes.

Top tips for strengthening the love and attachment between you and your child or young person

✓ Give your child positive attention as much as possible; catch them getting it right

✓ Go over the top when you see them. Let your eyes widen and your smile beam so that they recognise positive feelings within you

✓ Praise the values and the effort as well as the talent and skill. Don't use words like good or bad as this language begins to formulate who they think they are. Instead use specific praise like "I loved the fact that you brushed your teeth without me asking tonight, it shows you are taking responsibility for yourself. Well done."

✓ Acknowledge their feelings. Let them know you notice when they are happy, sad, worried, angry. Guide them through difficult feelings with reassurance and unconditional support. Be calm in difficult situations

✓ Reward them for making correct choices. This can be with a small gift, a cuddle, verbal praise or some special time together

✓ Children need structure as this makes them feel secure. Routines, boundaries and completion of tasks all help children feel confined and safe. Be clear and consistent in your approach, but be flexible

✓ Engage as much as possible with games, cuddles and, using their name to validate who they are

✓ Meet their basic needs with a nurturing approach – loving, caring, feeding, soothing and bathing children all communicate love

✓ Challenge the behaviour and not the person, aiming for win-win solutions

✓ Be patient – children perceive patience as love

Activities and questions for discussion with children and young people

1. What is love?

2. What does love feel like? Where do you feel it in your body?

3. Can you draw what love looks like?

4. Write down 5 ways you can show people that you love and care for them.

5. How does giving love feel?

6. Write down 5 ways people show that they love you.

7. How does receiving love feel?

Section 2 – Cognitive Behavioural Therapy (CBT) approaches to supporting feelings of love

CBT is a recognised therapeutic psychology model that helps us gain a deeper understanding of how our thoughts impact on how we feel and what we believe about ourselves and the world in which we live. There are two main principles of CBT:

1. Overly think something for a long period of time, we will eventually activate deeper feelings about the situation.

2. The longer we feel something, without interrupting the process, the more likely we are to believe it.

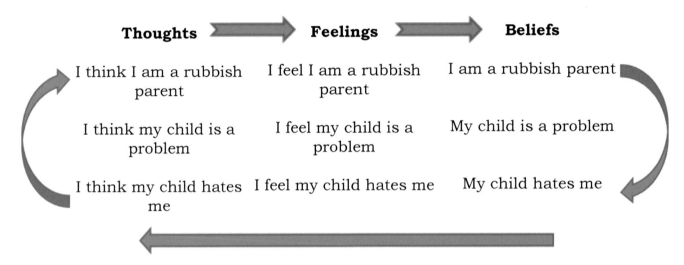

This negative cycle of thoughts, feelings and beliefs will eventually impact on actions and behaviours which in time could lead to even more devastating consequences. The positive element is that each stage can be interrupted and challenged so that we can weaken the current neurological circuit and develop newer more healthier ones over time.

Throughout the Love novel, Morna engages in lots of negative thinking patterns which activate many negative feelings but more so prevent her from absorbing the love that is around her. The combination of her thinking negatively about what those around her think and feel coupled with the bias thoughts she has about herself lead to Morna feeling unconnected from everyone, unloved and alone.

Lucy Love-Unlocker helps
Morna challenge some of
these perceptions and search
out evidence that establishes
newer, healthier thoughts and
feelings. Here are some of the
approaches that are introduced
throughout the book so that you
have a deeper insight, which is
essential if you want to support
your child's well-being as much

as possible. I have also included some philosophies that can help ensure that you and
your child's thoughts are on the right track.

Plant seeds of hope

As we all know, from tiny seeds grow enormous plants and trees; this same
analogy supports the development of our self-esteem and longer term emotional
well-being. Our role as parents, carers and professionals is to plant as many seeds
of positivity and hope as possible to create a mind that is colourful and bright,
rather than choked up with strangulating weeds.
Many of the children I work with latch onto the negative things that people
have said about them over their short life, which then filters the thoughts they
hear from then on. The life story of a very good friend of mine has had a major
influence on how I have engaged with children over the last 30 years and she is
happy for me to share it with you. I will call her Katherine.

Katherine grew up in the forces which meant her family moved around a lot.
Due to this, relationships with others were fleeting and she rarely felt settled and

secure. Her family dynamics were also very complex. Her dad was absent due to his role and had a problematic relationship with alcohol. Her mum struggled to be emotionally available due to the lifestyle that they had chosen and was often emotionally unstable and unpredictable. Katherine therefore didn't have a parent who was as emotionally present as she needed which impacted on her well-being, sense of self and over time, many life choices. At school Katherine struggled to focus, was often defiant and had no interest in achieving, as this wasn't something that was valued within her family. Teachers told her she was stupid, a waste of space who would never achieve anything and this she learned to believe. Feelings of hopelessness were planted inside Katherine and they grew into stronger thoughts which eventually led her and her best friend to run away at the age of 14. They were missing for several weeks.

Luckily, no harm came to the girls but returning home made things even more difficult as she felt she was now labelled even more negatively in school, which children cannot change alone. As she meandered through life doing low paid work, she craved love and security. She met a nice boy who was stable and kind and so married him and had children very young. She didn't know what love was but this felt okay and gave her two beautiful sons. However, Katherine yearned for more.

When she got to her mid-20s, she decided to risk doing an A-level. Her inner voice was telling her that she wouldn't be able to do it, she was stupid, but somewhere inside, Katherine felt like she could be more. She didn't have anything to lose. She succeeded in the A-level and then went on to do a degree, Masters and even began a PhD. She left her marriage but raised two amazing children and she began nurturing the seeds of her own mind. Katherine is one of the most intelligent, amazing, strong and beautiful women I know. She is highly successful in her field and has made herself a wonderful life. Yet what could Katherine have done if someone, just one person, had said "Katherine you have an awesome brain and if you use it, who knows what you could become", or even just "I love you and believe in you."

Even when disciplining children and young people, we can do it with hope. Rather than *"You are wasting your life and if you continue to do this, then your life will be a mess and you could end up in prison all because of these stupid choices that you are making."* Instead, we could say *"It's so frustrating for me to see someone with so much potential not using it. You have an ace brain, I'm not sure you realise how bright you are. Use it, make it work for you, I can help you. The future doesn't just happen, you create it. Let's make it brilliant, as that's what you deserve."*

Katherine's story affected me very deeply but also inspired me and motivated me to do something different. Over my time working with young people, I have made every effort to plant at least one positive seed for growth within that child's belief system. This is the power of positive psychology. If we give children hope for the future, then it lights the way and has a huge impact on the choices they make on their life journey. Furthermore, it embeds that they are capable of anything.

Over compensation

To be the parent or carer that our children need, we need to make sure that we have barricaded our own self-esteem. For those of you who remember Batfink with his amazing shield of steel, I sometimes feel that is what we all need as a rite of passage into parenting! Our children can hurt us very deeply as we are so emotionally entwined, but parenting must only ever go in one direction, from the parent to the child. They are the ones who need us and who need our emotional and nurturing flow in their direction.

If issues with our own self-esteem begin to dictate our parenting approaches, lots of problems can occur. If we find ourselves struggling to discipline in fear that our children may hate us and we don't feel strong enough to take that, then we need to grab our shield of steel. We are not the friends of our children, we are their champion and guide. It is highly likely that they will hate you sometimes and that means that you are doing it right and tweaking behaviours that may not benefit them long term.

Many of the children I have worked with over the years, especially those with severe emotional and behavioural difficulties, have often had love given to them in extreme material gifts. Parents have recognised that they love their children deep down, but often struggle to like them or be the parent they need to be due to the emotional baggage they have carried from their own childhood.

Love does not come packaged up in quad bikes, designer clothes, unrealistic amounts of Christmas and birthday money. Children don't need big gestures to show that you love them. Love is wrapped up in cuddles, kisses, words, actions, attention, time and meeting basic needs. Investment needs to be into their well-being account, not their financial account.

The Self-love Hook

In the Love novel, Lucy Lover-Unlocker attached a hook into Morna's brain where all the love around her could be hung and stored. The hook had two parts, one was for the words and gestures of others the other was for the positive words that Morna thought about herself.

In my work, I am helping children and parents to develop psychological hooks in order to hang praise, love and kindness on to. Unless these hooks have been developed, there is nowhere for positivity to stay.

At the heart of feeling love is feeling worthy of love and believing you are loveable. If we don't like who we are, how can we ever think anyone else can like us? Morna needed to like who she was and realise she was okay, which then helped her to accept the love of those around her. Developing a self-love hook means helping your children see their qualities, strengths, talents and skills. It is also about helping them to accept mistakes as part of learning rather than being a failure. This balance between liking who we are and being compassionate with our weaknesses, strengthens and develops the hook of self-love.

Top tips to foster positive expression and acceptance of love

- Improving the value of a young person takes time

- Every smile, positive comment, engaging conversation, listening if they are upset, comforting gesture if you know they seem unhappy, asking "How are you today", each second of forgiveness even if your last interaction was a nightmare, gives children and young people a currency which fosters feelings of worth

- We have all felt saddened when a child or young person shows total refusal to stop a behaviour when asked, but then someone else can ask and they do it straight away! The words exchanged are about 5% of the action; the quality of interactions prior to this event is the other 95%. A child who feels little about themselves will not want to let you down if you are the person who has invested in them, as you make them feel different, make them feel okay and that means the world to them

- Praise must be specific. Saying "that is good" does not register, as children do not usually feel good at or about anything. By being specific, e.g. "I really like the way that you have …", the young person is less likely to reject this praise

- Try it and see. Set yourself a personal challenge to engage positively with children and young people, even if you act it at the beginning, the results for you will make it worthwhile over time. Win win!

Questions for discussion with children and young people

1. What are your strengths, qualities, talents and skills?

2. What would you like to be better at?

3. Can you think of something that you failed at recently? What was it?

4. What did you learn from this situation?

5. Write down three positive things that people have said about you.

6. How could these seeds of positivity grow into making your future a better one?

6. How could these seeds of positivity grow into making your future a better one?

Section 3 - How feeling unloved affects behaviour, self-esteem and emotional development

Love is at the very heart of who we feel we are, what we feel we are capable of, the quality of the relationships around us, our well-being and our ability to cope with life's ups and downs. It also activates our emotional development, contributes to our personality traits and behaviours and impacts on how the brain manages and deals with emotions.

Love is related to all the Blinks' books in this series, as it can have a role on how each emotion manifests and presents:

> ➤ If we are feeling worried and anxious all the time, it can be due to not feeling secure in ourselves at that time

> ➤ Anger is often underpinned with feelings of failure which is a symptom of weakened self-love

> ➤ When we feel sad, we are more likely to emotionally withdraw which leads to emotional attachments deteriorating as well as our perception of self being damaged too

> ➤ Self-esteem is based on the opinion we have of ourselves and those around us. If we are unable to recognise the language of love from others, we could feel less loveable. This in itself will drive lower levels of the love we need to feel for ourselves

> ➤ Children who feel shy and/or socially anxious are very aware and often feel that it is down to failure on their part. This nervous behaviour around others can affect how children reach out and tap into the love around them, or demonstrate the act of giving love which is equally important

From the above list, we can see how important it is for all of us to engage in acts of giving and receiving love in order to maximise our chances of living as wholesome a life as possible and coping with the demands of this, at times, crazy world. However, life isn't a fairy tale and there can be many complex variables, developmental issues and emotional blocks as to why the river of love doesn't flow so freely.

Emotional Blocks to letting love in

As human beings it is recognised that we have an innate craving to feel loved and accepted. If we receive higher levels of negativity, criticism and rejection in our early years, this desire to search out for what we most need can become damaged very early on, which will then activate a barrier of defence to protect us from further pain. It seems natural to have a mechanism that shields our feelings from hurt but the default setting can also prevent us from feeling loved and accepted too.

This emotional block will prevent you from receiving compliments and or dealing with positive attention. Therefore, with children, it is crucial that we use specific rather than general praise. Using words like good and bad will readily be rejected by anyone who has emotional barriers to feeling loved and accepted. Instead we need to praise the process or pick out specific areas for praise which is less likely to be rejected, as Lucy Love-Unlocker explains in the Love novel. This process strengthens the psychological hooks that we can hang the praise onto which will keep it around for longer and foster improved self-esteem, rather than it dispersing quickly into the ether of the mind! This practice is fundamental, like planting seeds of hope to help us develop a more positive inner message of who we become to believe we are, and more importantly, our ability to accept that we are okay and worthy of love.

Bitter and angry or search to heal

In the previous section, I shared Katherine's story with you. Another very good friend of mine, I will call her A'ishah, is again one of the most intelligent, insightful and beautifully-soled women I know. She also had a very difficult start in life and has also been an inspiration in the work I do with children and young people, as her story helps children understand that life can change, which helps them start to heal with hope.

A'ishah was the first born to a mum who had severe learning difficulties and was probably functioning as an eight-year-old intellectually and emotionally. A'ishah's mum was unable to be the mum she needed. There was little emotional warmth or nurture from her but A'ishah continued to yearn for it. One day when she was five, A'ishah was called into the kitchen by her mum. There was something different in her voice that day and A'ishah thought that this was the day she was going to tell her that she loved her. Her mum beckoned and asked A'ishah to stand in front of her with her eyes closed. Excitedly, A'ishah did so and as her mum had one hand behind her back, she thought it was to receive a gift. A'ishah's mum then cut off her eyelashes. This act was one of many that A'ishah experienced and which symbolised her mum's inability to show her love.

Luckily A'ishah's Dad did show love to her and they had a true bond. However, this could never compensate for the extreme negative parenting she received from her mum. For most of her life, A'ishah has struggled with feeling loved and yet has the heart of a lion. She gives so freely to others in her community to anyone in need, such as refugees, children and young people. A'ishah gives a lot of love as she needs a lot of love, and in some way these acts satisfy an acceptance and validity of who she is.

Life is hard and we need to visualise difficult situations as manure that can feed our growth and development. They can teach us, motivate, scaffold and strengthen who we are. Katharine and A'ishah have both spent a lifetime trying to heal, rectify and improve. They could quite easily, I am sure you would agree, have become angry, bitter and resentful women which would have kept them living in that upsetting past. Instead, they reflected and accepted their reality and over time, this helped them to release their negative emotions and gain some of the emotional freedom they both deserve.

Attachment and individual differences

As stated in the introduction of this section, loving attachments are significant to how we develop across the lifespan. It is important to note here that the bond with our children can also vary along the way. A strong emotional bond in the early years can become challenged as children hit developmental stages along the way, with adolescence being one of the most significant for us all. This does not signify a permanent severing of closeness between, or an irreversible change in, how you react together. However, changes can happen if we don't work hard to get things back as they were.

One young person, who I worked with for several years from the age of 14, had broken relationships with every member of his family, so much so that he was no longer invited on family birthdays. The degree of parental monitoring had stopped and he came and went as he chose and avoided interaction as much as possible. One day, I sat and talked with his mum to see why things had become so difficult with her son. His mum spoke very openly and honestly about at time when he was eight years old and she said he woke up horrible and he has been that way ever since.

This was one of the saddest things I had ever heard. The young man in question, I will call him Ed, didn't wake up a horrible person on that day. It is much more likely that he woke up feeling sad, anxious, lonely and emotionally distressed which probably fuelled angry behaviours. At this time, Ed was in desperate need for an emotional connection to help him understand these difficult feelings and not feel even worse because of them. Ed was a beautiful young man, sensitive, intelligent, thoughtful and loyal with incredibly strong values. Sadly, his complex home life activated high social anxiety, school avoidance, rock bottom self-esteem and high risk-taking behaviours which led to involvement with the police. It was like Ed was in a parallel universe with who he could be and what he could achieve.

This is why it is crucial not to engage in biased thinking patterns, such as mindreading, when our children misbehave as this can begin the cycle of negativity that becomes the norm and then impacts on the individual differences that children present with. Other ways in which poor emotional connection with caregivers could impact on personality traits are:

- ✓ struggling to negotiate emotionally with carers

- ✓ finding it difficult to identify own wants and needs

- ✓ struggling to understand the thoughts, feelings and needs of others

- ✓ perceiving themselves as powerless or over-powerful/dangerous

- ✓ being superficially engaging, charming (phoney)

- ✓ avoiding eye contact

- ✓ being indiscriminately affectionate with strangers, vulnerable to grooming and radicalisation

- ✓ lacking the ability to give or receive affection (i.e. will not be 'cuddly')

- ✓ exhibiting extreme control problems - often manifesting in devious ways (e.g. stealing from family; secret solvent abuse, etc.)

- ✓ being destructive to self and others

- ✓ lack of kindness (cruelty) to animals

- ✓ displaying erratic behaviour, tell lies

- ✓ having poor impulse controls and ability to self-regulate

- ✓ lacking cause and effect thinking

✓ having a weaker conscience

✓ displaying abnormal eating patterns

✓ showing poor peer relationships

✓ being pre-occupied with fire, blood and gore

✓ asking persistent nonsense questions and incessant chatter

✓ being inappropriately demanding and clingy

✓ having abnormal speech patterns

✓ displaying passive aggression (provoking anger in others)

✓ having less trust in others

✓ showing signs of low mood and depression

✓ exhibiting pseudo-maturity (acting like someone of an older age)

✓ having low self esteem

✓ showing signs of a guilt complex

✓ showing signs of repressed anger

✓ sabotaging placements such as school, foster family, etc.

The diagram on the following page shows how different attachment phases can drive individual differences in children, young people and adults.

Attachment phase

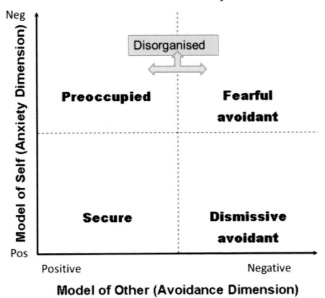

Each phase will now be explained using research findings from John Bowlby's theory paradigm (1969).

Secure Attachment – protective factor

Parent opinions & approaches in childhood	Early adulthood	Later adulthood
<ul><li>Felt positive about birth</li><li>Let children explore</li><li>Intervene when needed</li></ul>	<ul><li>More resilient</li><li>Focus on learning</li><li>Self regulate</li><li>Positive relationships with peers</li><li>Follow gender rules</li><li>Leadership qualities</li></ul>	<ul><li>Social competence</li><li>Positive relationships with others</li><li>Positive romantic relationships</li><li>Marital satisfaction</li></ul>

Avoidant/dismissive Attachment – Risk factor

Parent opinions & approaches in childhood	Early adulthood	Later adulthood
• Mums struggling with parenthood • Tense & irritable • Pushed children away readily	• Counselling intervention suggested by counsellor • Low compliance • Whingey	• Depression • Increased chances of conduct disorders • Increased anger due to emotional unavailability

Anxious/preoccupied Attachment – Risk factor

Parent opinions & approaches in childhood	Early adulthood	Later adulthood
• Parents pushed children towards independence too quickly	• Expressive in distress • Sought counsellor intervention • Passive • Easily frustrated in challenges	• Depression • Potential risk for mental health problems • Constant attachment seeking with others – draining emotionally

Disorganised/fearful Attachment – Risk factor

Parent opinions & approaches in childhood	Early adulthood	Later adulthood
• Maltreatment by parents • Intrusive approach • Inconsistent parenting	• Disassociation • Greater risk of self harm • Increased risk of personality disorders • Risk of development of eating disorders	• Greatest predictor for maturity problems • Higher risk of mental health problems

These attachment behaviours can also predict:
- separation behaviour at airports
- likelihood of rebound relationships
- sexual infidelity
- sense of self and well-being
- coping strategies
- interpretations of facial expressions

It is a natural part of growing up for all children and young people to display some of these things sometimes. It may it not be due to a poor emotional connection with the caregiver. However, it is the recognition and reflection of these developmental issues that demand our attention so that we can support, tweak and direct children and young people with love and nurture, so that these become healthier traits across the lifespan.

Attachment and emotional development

Those who are familiar with the Blinks' reference manuals will no doubt be experts on the Emotional Development Cycle created by Levin (1982). For those of you who are still eager and open to learning about such issues, and I'm assuming you are as you're reading this manual right now, here is a table which shows the developmental phases that children go through and what they need from us to scaffold well-being.

Gaps in emotional growth (non-typical development)	Stage	Affirmations needed from Parent/carer to child	Healthy emotional growth (typical development)
Developmental block = **Don't exist, don't be, don't trust** • Withdrawn, nervous, scared of change, • Does not recognise own needs, does not call for care • Repeated oral behaviours	**Being** **(birth-** **6 months)**	Emotional need = **contact** ✓ I'm glad you are here ✓ You belong ✓ Your needs are important to me ✓ You can feel all of your feelings ✓ We want to care for you	• Confident & trusting • Embraces new experiences and relationships • Aware of own needs, signals any distress, asks for help
Developmental block = **Don't be active, don't do** • Passive, quiet, holds back • Struggles to settle and engage • Responds with extremes	**Doing** **(6-18months)**	Emotional need = **stimulus** ✓ You can explore, we will keep you safe ✓ You can try things as many times as you need ✓ You can be interested in everything ✓ I love watching you grow and learn	• Curious, creative, use their initiative • Active, easily stimulated, enjoy sensory experiences • Enjoy being involved & likes to experiment
Developmental block = **don't think** • Oppositional to requests, acts strong and tough • Directive towards others • Demanding, pushy • Overreacts • Can feel a victim	**Thinking** **(18months-** **3 years)**	Emotional need = **structure** ✓ I am glad you are starting to think for yourself ✓ You can say no and push the limits ✓ It's okay to be angry but I won't let you hurt yourself or others ✓ You can know what you need and ask for help ✓ You can be yourself and I will still care for you	• Can think, express and deal with emotions • Understands cause and effect, basic rules • Can think for themselves and say no

Gaps in emotional growth (non-typical development)	Stage	Affirmations needed from Parent/carer to child	Healthy emotional growth (typical development)
Developmental block = **don't be who you are, don't be you** • Overpowering, threatening, bullying, lies • Low self-confidence and self-esteem • Boasts reputation to bolster identity	**Identity & Power (3-6 years)**	Emotional need = **recognition** ✓ You can explore who you are and find out about others ✓ You can try out different ways of using your power ✓ All of your feelings are okay ✓ You can learn from the results of your behaviour	• Sound sense of self has own identity • Understands different roles and relationships • Recognises actions, behaviours and consequences in context
Developmental block = **don't make mistakes** • Struggles with authority and rules • Mismatch between expectations and skills • Very laid back, over casual • Does not finish tasks	**Skills & Structure (6-12 years)**	Emotional need = **excitement, frequency** ✓ It is ok to stop and think before you respond with yes and no ✓ Mistakes are good, they mean that you are learning ✓ You can trust your instinct to decide what to do ✓ You can find ways of doing things that are good for you ✓ You can learn when and how to disagree ✓ You can decide when to get help rather than stay distressed ✓ We always want to be with you and it is okay to differ, that is when we can learn more about each other together	• Embraces diversity and difference • Recognises own internal/external structure of values/ codes of conduct • Identifies with same sex group

Gaps in emotional growth (non-typical development)	Stage	Affirmations needed from Parent/carer to child	Healthy emotional growth (typical development)
Developmental block = **don't grow up** • Engages in inappropriate risk-taking behaviours • Poor relationships • Struggles to separate	**Integration** **(Separation & Sexuality)** **(12-18 years)**	Emotional need = **sex, freedom,** ✓ You can know who you are and learn practise skills for being independent ✓ You can develop your own relationships and interests ✓ You can grow and develop in your gender role, but it is ok to still need help ✓ You can adapt old skills to create new ways ✓ We are excited by who you will become as an adult ✓ We trust that you will ask for support when you need it	• Enjoys being who they are • Embraces independence • Developing a confident sexual identity • Engages in challenges and new experiences

From this invaluable information, which helps to support the nurture principles, we can see that there are four key components that are vital from us so that our children can progress at the expected phases of development.

Attunement
- 'Tuning' into emotional state, tone, pitch, rhythm – child feels received and understood

Containment
- Adult's capacity to withstand and hold steady in the face of the child's raw feeling states they are communicating. Shows emotional state is survivable

Calming and soothing
- Helps the child to manage their emotional and physical states of hyper-arousal and to return to a peaceful state of regulation

Validation
- Catches the child's emotional experience, demonstrates understanding and acceptance. Support the child to stay with their authentic experience

This important role of helping children to understand their thoughts and feelings becomes the back bone to children regulating their behaviours by recognising that they have a choice.

Feelings, Thoughts and Behaviours

When children feel confident to make the right choices quickly and easily, we can regard them as being emotionally mature and having a good sense of self-esteem, resilience and well-being which can buffer the difficult times they will experience in life over which we have no control or ability to protect them from.

My mum has often commented how glad she is that she isn't raising my sister and I at this time, due to all the societal issues children and young people face compared to when we were younger. I cannot shield my children from the world and what it may expose them to. I simply hope that I have invested enough into them emotionally that they can make the right choices in life and bounce back when necessary, so that life blips don't turn into catastrophes.

Top tips to support and strengthen feeling loved

- Tell them what behaviours annoy/irritate and tell them why. They can't change behaviours they do not recognise as causing problems
- Allow your emotions to be seen (anger, frustration, sadness, happiness, etc) appropriately: teachers are people too
- Confront feelings in an open, honest way and help to build positive relationships
- Anticipate their behaviours; let them know you are doing this
- Have a good working relationship with families, parents, social workers etc
- Listen to the young person and hear what they have to say. But remember, they communicate in more ways than just verbally
- Plan with them for their adult life; help them to understand how they can be positive in the role of adult
- Remember that the adult is responsible for helping young people make

appropriate, positive attachments

- Give the young person a safe, secure environment to express their innermost feelings, fears, hurt, etc
- Don't presume that children understand emotions, help them name and claim feelings which is very empowering
- Age isn't a number, it is a state of mind
- Try to match your expectations to where you think a child is emotionally – this helps them feel attuned to you
- Use emotional literacy wherever possible to educate them about feelings and emotions. For example, "you look angry, I can see why you are feeling angry and that is okay, but I cannot let you hurt yourself or other people when you are feeling like this." Why not try asking if this is this worth it, instead breathing deeply in and slowly out and then letting the feeling go

Section 4 – Your role in supporting children who have difficulty feeling love or are emotionally detached

As a teacher, psychologist, author and parent, being a parent is by far the hardest role of all. Our children can make us joyfully happy and proud, activating the deepest, purest, primitive form of love that is unrivalled. However, children can also activate feelings we may have never experienced before, such as frustration, anger, exhaustion and emotional overload. All of these emotions are a natural and normal part of parenting, as our children are emotionally entwined with who we are from the moment we conceive.

The psychology of parenting is very underrated. No one prepares you for the personal journey that you will go on, in the developing role of becoming a parent or carer. At many times, I found myself wrestling with my own selfishnesses to become the mum I wanted to be.

Parenting, as hard has it has been at times, has changed me for the better. I have learned to loosen rigid preferences and personality traits that motherhood wasn't going to get along with. I remember when my daughter was only a few months old. I was making the most of the time when she was having her afternoon nap. The washing was on and I was in the kitchen washing the dishes to go into the afternoon feeling ordered and organised. I have always been the kind of person who likes to sit down and relax when everything is done. This routine usually worked well and gave me a sense of achievement, in the craziness of having your first child.

This one day, my daughter woke up earlier than usual. The dishes weren't finished and for a split second I felt frustrated as I couldn't complete the task in hand. I went and picked her out of her cot and carried her downstairs for her feed. As I looked at her suckling away, a part of me wished she had woken up five minutes later so that I could have finished the dishes and enjoyed this time more. Then the reality hit me. This was my child who was dependent on me and needed feeding; what I was doing was allowing my behaviour preferences to affect this moment. I needed to get tough on my inner personality master and ask her to loosen up. My role had changed and it demanded flexibility.

As hard as it was at times, adapting from being self-sufficient, independent and with limited responsibilities, becoming a parent has helped me soften some of my traits for the better. Interestingly, it is also suggested that women's IQs also increase after having children. Intelligence is based on our ability to adapt and perhaps because parenthood demands the biggest adaptions we will ever make, our brain capacity and capability improves because of it!

Reasons parents can struggle to love their children
Parenting demands a lot from us and is what children need to develop their sense of self and well-being. However, we can love our children with all our heart but still not be able to give our time freely or adapt as necessary to be the attuned parent our children need.

Parenting with low self-esteem makes the process much more complicated as it affects our judgement and our ability to be tough at times, in case it means our children might not like us. Sometimes the children who I work with tell me how they can't wait to become parents as they will have someone who loves them always. For those of you reading this book, who are parents already, you will understand that parenting is about giving, not receiving, for many years. Children only begin to understand the significance and importance of love from around nine years old. It is important to remember here that parenting must be one directional: from parent to child. We must make every effort to not incorporate our own needs or begin needing from our children, as this interrupts the positive parenting model.

One issue many parents can also struggle with is projecting our own negative traits onto our child. If we struggle to like who we are, then we will struggle to like those traits in our children. We must remember however, that they are not us and they are not experiencing the same life as us. Although there might be similarities, these can be due to natural development or a genetic trait and not always because you have got something terribly wrong. The important thing here is not why our children are doing what they are doing, it is what can we do tweak the behaviour to help them develop in the right direction.

For many of us, having children activates our assessment of the parenting we received. We reflect on what we think our parents did well and would like to continue. We also reflect on some of the parenting we would choose to reject and do differently. We must remember here not to let the parenting pendulum swing too far in the opposite direction. Sitting in the middle with a balanced approach to situations is often the most beneficial.

Back to the Batfink shield of steel: this is what we need to do to set personal boundaries in order to protect our own feelings so that we do what is right, retaining our long-term vision of what we would like our children to be in the future.

Top tips for promoting giving and receiving love
- Help children to love who they are. Celebrate their positives and accept their negatives. Help children and young people, as well as yourself, to loosen the idea of perfection by knowing you are okay is more than good enough
- Help children take on challenges they will succeed in, as this builds confidence and a sense of pride in who they are
- Teach children to talk themselves up rather than down
- Help children to see that asking for help is a sign of strength and not weakness

- Communicate love and remind children of the language of love and what love is and is not. Love is not hurting others, love should not be conditional and should not feel like it is only one-sided

- Teach children and young people how to strengthen relationships by having meaningful conversations with others. This can be done easily if we learn to show an interest in others and ask questions about the other person. This makes relationships feel purposeful and reciprocal

- Help children clear some of the mental clutter that can act as a block to letting love in

- Help children change their thoughts about who cares about them and what they deserve. This will activate healthier, happier beliefs and a sense of well-being

- Reduce judgemental thinking. Judging others makes us feel judged, so make more of a conscious effort to give more positive love to the world and you will feel it back two-fold

- We all need to give the love we need. If we feel people don't show us enough love, then we need to ask ourselves if we show enough love to that person

Questions for discussion with children and young people

1. Write down all the people who you know love and care about you. Now create a paper chain and write each person on a link. This is your chain of support and it is important to remember they are all there for you whenever you need them.

2. Write a list of all things that you have experienced that have made your life great. Remember these things on difficult days as a catalogue of your wonderful life.

3. Think about questions you could ask a new person about their life that would show that you are interested in getting to know them. Make a list now, as you never know when you might need to remember some of the things on the list!

4. What have you achieved in your lifetime? All of your achievements are successes

and a credit to you. Make a list of everything that you can do now that you couldn't do when you were a baby.

5. Think of a mistake you have made lately, or something you are struggling with:

- What have you learned from the process?

- What possible solutions are there to the problem? Circle the one you think would be the best to try, then give it go and see

Summary

For some of you, this manual may have been a tough read as it may have opened your eyes to some of the things that we do and now realise we could do better. If you have had that thought, then that in itself makes you an ace parent, carer or professional. That element of reflection and insight is what makes you the best you can be. It will not buffer you from mistakes but it will stop you from making the same mistakes and help you get back on track as quickly as possible, hopefully to head in a more positive direction.

I haven't met a parent yet who didn't love their child; weakened attachment certainly doesn't reflect lack of love. However, the attunement we have with our children communicates the love our children need to feel. I hope this book has helped everyone not to love more, but just love in a way that gives us the most emotional reward: happier, emotionally attached children and young people and happier, emotionally resilient parents.

Love Summary Checklist – little things that can help in a big way!
- It's not the quantity of time you spend with children, it's the quality. Try and spend special time with your child as this strengthens your relationship and makes your child more likely to turn to you in times of emotional distress. Talk, play, listen and support, as this shows children that you like being with them which in turn makes them feel loveable and valued
- Think positively about your child and communicate it too. Children can be annoying and make mistakes but they often hear if negative things are said about them, which impacts on their sense of self. None of us like our negative traits bandied around and children are even more sensitive to this
- Be generous in how you give love. Tell them, cuddle and kiss them, give them little gestures of kindness, listen attentively, be there when they are worried or

sad, be patient when they are angry and difficult, build them up, celebrate their qualities. These actions all communicate high quality love

- Remember you are the adult and children need to know that so that they feel secure and in good hands. You need to be their safe base otherwise it can effect the equilibrium of parenting

- Do what I say and what I do! Model the behaviours you would like your child to develop, be positive, respectful, kind, committed and caring. By doing so you embed feelings of self-worth within them which they will go on to share with others

- Protect them always, but also from unnecessary information. Our job is to protect their innocence for as long as possible, not to destroy it with information they do not need to know or are too young to process or understand

- Let children be who they are. Yes, we need to tweak through a nurturing approach but your child isn't you and needs to develop into the best of who they can be, which might be different to what you want them to be

- Tell children loving stories from when they were young. This reminds them of the love and happy memories that they have implanted in you and makes them feel valued and special

- Remember you are the parent your role is to give to them, by being emotionally available and present, not for them to feed your emotional needs

- If your child pushes you in to not liking them at times, recognise it and even if you need to act, try to see the positive in your child again as quickly as possible. Otherwise what is already difficult could become much worse

- Always try to remember children are children, not adults. The choices they make are not with an adult brain. Don't mindread negatively into the reason for their actions as, due to negative labelling, this could affect you responding accurately

- Put yourself in their shoes. Take yourself back to when you were a child and how it felt when you were told off, or even when your curiosity took charge and you did something with impulse and excitement rather than with logic and moral reasoning. Try to remember this when disciplining children, as they are learning with every action and actions are not always deliberate

- Remember to check in with yourself. It is often the case that what we don't like in others is what we, deep down, don't like in ourselves. Our children will do things that remind us of our negative traits. Be gentle and compassionate with yourself and your child, to accept who you both are, flaws and all!

- Love and then love some more. Love with warmth, openness, availability and kindness. Love emotionally, verbally and physically. Remember, love is all you need!

If you and your child have enjoyed The Blinks – Love (book 6) then look out for the other books in the series, The Blinks – Worry, The Blinks - Anger, The Blinks – Self-esteem, The Blinks – Sad and The Blinks – Shy which are all readily available online at www.theblinks.co.uk and in book stores.

To get in touch on social media, please go to:

Facebook - /Theblinksbooks
Twitter - @BlinksThe

OTHER TITLES IN THE SERIES

The Blinks novels are for children age 7 and upwards. Younger children would benefit when reading the novel with adults as it's never too young to start emotional dialogues - there is no upper age range as no matter your age the core of emotions feels the same.

The Blinks are created from morsels of goodness that all the good folk who have ever lived, leave to the Universe. These could have been left behind by people who you have loved in the past. Their whole purpose is to share their wisdom and kindness with children who need support and guidance in order to promote positive well-being. 'The Blinks – Worry' is the first novel in the Blinks series of books. The first book in the series to help all children and young people understand how worry and anxiety present. It is written as a fiction book with many messages and guidance woven into the stories about Amanda and her friends.

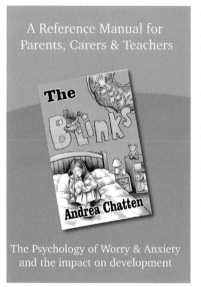

The Blinks books were created to help children, young people and their families understand emotional and behavioural issues. More so, it was to provide strategies and techniques to help manage and change the intensity and duration of problematic behaviours over time. This supportive book provides a deeper understanding of psychology of worrying and how it can impact on other developmental issues including self-esteem and emotions. It also provides lots of 'top tips' of what works best for children and young people whilst growing up, and some activity questions that can be used as a starting point to initiate emotive dialogue or discussion with children.

Robbie's life has never been great, but the events over the last few years have slowly made him more and more unhappy and angry. One day it all gets too much and his anger erupts! A sequence of wrong choices leaves Robbie with a string of problems that need sorting out. Luckily Chika Change-Your-thoughts sees that he needs help at this difficult time. Together with Cale, 'the community bad lad with a heart', Robbie learns just who is responsible for his anger and how to deal with it.

This supportive booklet accompanies the book 'The Blinks – Anger' written specifically for older children and those in their early teens. It provides a deeper understanding of the psychology of anger for parents, carers and teachers, and how anger can impact on other developmental issues and all other emotions. It also provides lots of 'top tips' on what works best for children and young people whilst growing up and some activity questions that can be used as a starting point to initiate emotive dialogue or discussion with children.

In 'The Blinks – Self Esteem' Edition Bladen and Tim are twins who have spent many years being unkind to each other. This has not helped them develop very positive feelings about themselves. This low self-esteem has affected their confidence, friendships, who they believe they are and their happiness. Things have been difficult for many years, but then the unthinkable happens, and Bladen and Tim think that it is their fault. This causes them to dislike themselves even more. Larry Love-Who-You-Are recognises this difficult situation and works hard to help the twins and himself overcome some very personal challenges. This book is for children aged 7+ who want help with learning how to cope with low self-esteem. It is written as a fiction book with lots of messages and guidance woven into the stories about Bladen and Tim and their friends.

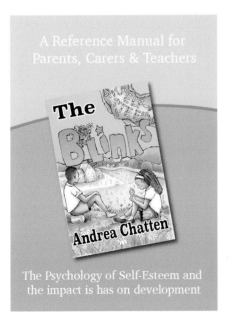

This supportive booklet accompanies the novel 'The Blinks – Self-Esteem' written specifically for children and those in their early teens. It provides a deeper understanding of the psychology of low self-esteem for parents, carers and teachers, and how this can impact on other developmental issues and all other emotions. It also provides lots of 'top tips' on what works best for children and young people whilst growing up and some activity questions that can be used as a starting point to initiate emotive dialogue or discussion with children.

Shan is a normal girl in many ways, who has a normal life, but one thing Shan has which many other children don't is buckets and buckets of sadness. Over time Shan has managed to collect many sad memories which replay constantly in her mind and make her feel sad. Things start to get more difficult when one day at school, when given a very important job, Shan makes a seriously wrong choice and is found out by one of her classmates. Shan feels so sad and worried that she becomes ill and hides away in bed, unable to face going to school. Thankfully, Marlowe Mindful sees Shan as someone who is ready for Blinks' support and begins the process of helping her understand her sadness and how to change her feelings for the better.

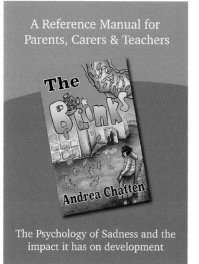

This supportive booklet accompanies the book 'The Blinks – Sad' written specifically for children and those in their early teens. It provides a deeper understanding of the psychology of sadness for parents, carers and teachers, and how sadness can impact on other developmental issues and all other emotions. It also provides lots of 'top tips' on what works best for children and young people whilst growing up and some activity questions that can be used as a starting point to initiate emotive dialogue or discussion with children.

Nazim has always been shy but the older he gets, the more he begins to hate his shyness. It makes him lack in confidence and leaves it difficult for him to make eye contact, which means he feels awkward around others. His shyness dominates all his thoughts and behaviours which are overwhelming and the bigger the problem gets for him, the less he talks. Then he decides not to talk at all. Time for some Blink intervention!

Blink 24399 Colin Confidence sees a need to help Nazim and teaches him to see his shyness as a special quality that should be celebrated in this loud and fast world. On his journey, Nazim learns many things about himself. He is given tips to help him manage his own shyness at difficult times, and this helps to make his life better all round. Along the way, Colin Confidence is surprised to experience a few things he didn't even plan for!

This supportive booklet accompanies the book 'The Blinks – Shy' written specifically for children and those in their early teens.

It provides a deeper understanding of the psychology of shyness for parents, carers and teachers, and how shyness can impact on other developmental issues and all other emotions. It also provides lots of 'top tips' on what works best for children and young people whilst growing up and some activity questions that can be used as a starting point to initiate emotive dialogue or discussion with children.

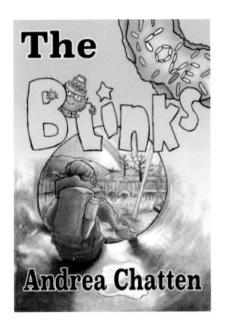

Morna, on the surface, is just like you and me, but there is something that she has struggled with for a long time. Morna finds it difficult to feel love. She is surrounded by a big family, and many siblings who all love her dearly but sadly she just can't feel it. This issue brings many problems and one day when she feels the most alone she has ever felt; she runs away.

Whilst trying to find a hiding place in the park she unknowingly disturbs Blink 16225 Lucy Love-Unlocker who becomes concerned. This isn't the usual way that Blinks find children and young people to work with, but when Morna is discussed with Chief Blink, they agree they need to begin as soon as possible. However, things get a lot worse before they get better, resulting in the police becoming involved!

As the friendship between them develops, Morna learns a lot about the language of love and how those around her show it. More importantly, she learns lots of important skills that enable her to feel love and to keep the feeling locked in her for as long as possible.

TO PURCHASE ANY OF THE BOOKS IN THE SERIES GO TO:
www.theblinks.co.uk
Also available in print and on Amazon and as Kindle versions.